Which Way Bunny?

A lift-the-flap book about left and right

by Mavis Smith

Little Hippo

"Wake up, Ben Bunny!" cried a little black crow.
"Someone took your carrot, and I thought
 you should know."

Ben Bunny jumped up. "Which way did he go?"
"He went to the RIGHT," replied the crow.

"Faster, Ben," cried the crow.

"Go LEFT again, you're much too slow."

"Hurry, Ben, go to the RIGHT.
Don't let that rabbit out of your sight."

"Go, Ben Bunny – straight down that hole,
and take back what that rabbit stole!"